C000057145

Collins Primary Maths ▽4▽
Extension Copymasters

Series Editor: Peter Clarke

Authors: Andrew Edmondson, Elizabeth Jurgensen,
Jeanette Mumford, Sandra Roberts

Contents

41	Calculate and order	To order a set of whole numbers less than 10 000.	Su 1, 2
42	Find the missing multiple	To use known number facts and place value to add or subtract mentally: continue to add or subtract two-digit multiples of 10, add or subtract a pair of multiples of 100, crossing 1000.	Su 2, 1
43	Complete the calculations	To use known number facts and place value to add or subtract mentally: add or subtract any pair of two-digit numbers, including crossing the tens boundary.	Su 2, 5
44	Adding three numbers	To develop and refine written methods for column addition of two whole numbers less than 1000, and addition of more than two such numbers.	Su 3, 1
45	Solving problems	To use addition and subtraction to solve word problems involving numbers in "real life" or money, using one or more steps.	Su 3, 5
46	Measuring cylinders	To know the equivalent of one half, one quarter, three quarters and one tenth of 1 litre in ml.	Su 4, 1
47	Measuring displacement	To record estimates and readings from scales to a suitable degree of accuracy: record measurements using mixed units, or the nearest whole/half/quarter unit (e.g. 3·25 litres).	Su 4, 5
48	Reflecting shapes	To sketch the reflection of a simple shape in a mirror line parallel to one side (all sides parallel or perpendicular to the mirror line).	Su 5, 1
49	Stained glass fanlights	To solve mathematical shape problems or puzzles, recognise and explain patterns and relationships, generalise and predict; suggest extensions by asking "What if...?"	Su 6, 1
50	New patterns from old	To solve mathematical shape problems or puzzles, recognise and explain patterns and relationships, generalise and predict; suggest extensions by asking "What if...?"	Su 6, 2
51	Sorting multiples of 2, 3, 4, 5 and 10	To recognise multiples of 2, 3, 4, 5 and 10, up to the tenth multiple.	Su 7, 3
52	Missing numbers	To solve mathematical problems or puzzles, recognise and explain patterns and relationships, generalise and predict. Suggest extensions by asking "What if...?"	Su 7, 5
53	Simple sevens	To begin to know the multiplication facts for the 7 times table.	Su 8, 4
54	Multiplying larger numbers	To know by heart multiplication facts for 2, 3, 4, 5 and 10 times tables.	Su 8, 5
55	Multiplication and division	To use known number facts and place value to multiply and divide integers, including by 10 and then 100 (whole number answers).	Su 9, 3
56	Recording division	To develop and refine written methods for TU ÷ U.	Su 9, 4
57	Heads up	To begin to use ideas of simple proportion: for example, "one in every...".	Su 10, 2
58	Rugby decimals	To begin to use ideas of simple proportion: for example, "one in every...".	Su 10, 5
59	Missing numbers	To develop and refine written methods for column addition of two whole numbers less than 1000, and addition of more than two such numbers.	Su 11, 2
60	Travel Venn and Carroll diagrams	To solve a problem by collecting quickly, organising, representing and interpreting data in tables, charts, graphs and diagrams, including those generated by a computer, for example: Venn and Carroll diagrams (two criteria).	Su 12, 5

Name _____ Date _____

Roundabouts

1 Round these weights to the nearest 10 g.

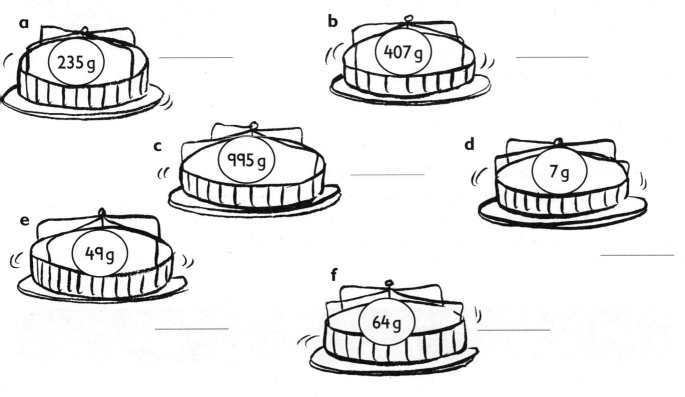

a (235 g) _____

b (407 g) _____

c (995 g) _____

d (7 g) _____

e (49 g) _____

f (64 g) _____

2 Look at the lengths below. Round each length to the nearest 10 m.

3 Round your answer to the nearest 100 m.

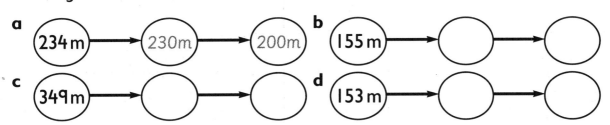

a (234 m) → (230 m) → (200 m)

b (155 m) → ( ) → ( )

c (349 m) → ( ) → ( )

d (153 m) → ( ) → ( )

4 Write an amount of paint that could be in the can.

a 500 ml to the nearest 100 ml.

463 ml

b 340 ml to the nearest 10 ml.

c 700 ml to the nearest 100 ml.

d 60 ml to the nearest 10 ml.

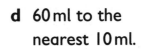

e 1000 ml to the nearest 100 ml.

f 200 ml to the nearest 10 ml.

Collins Primary Maths © HarperCollins*Publishers* Ltd 2000

Name _____ Date _____

Target 100

A game for 2 players
You will need a pack of 0–9 number cards.

Instructions

● Shuffle the cards and deal them out between you.

● Look at your cards and use some or all of them to make
  an addition calculation with the answer as close to 100
  as you can.

● Record and answer the calculation in the record sheet below.

● If you have made 100 exactly, you get two points.

● If neither of you have made 100, the player with the number
  closest to 100 gets one point.

● Play 10 rounds. The player with the most points is the winner.

Round	Player A		Player B	
	Calculation	Points	Calculation	Points
1				
2				
3				
4				
5				
6				
7				
8				
9				
10				
		Total		**Total**

Collins Primary Maths © HarperCollins*Publishers* Ltd 2000

Name _____ Date _____

Motorbike race

A game for 2 players

You will need: a 0–9 die and a blank die labelled in multiples of 10 (10–60)

How to play:

● Start at the beginning of the number line.

● Throw the dice to make a two-digit number (6 and 30 would make 36) and add your total to the start number.

● The first player to reach 1000 is the winner.

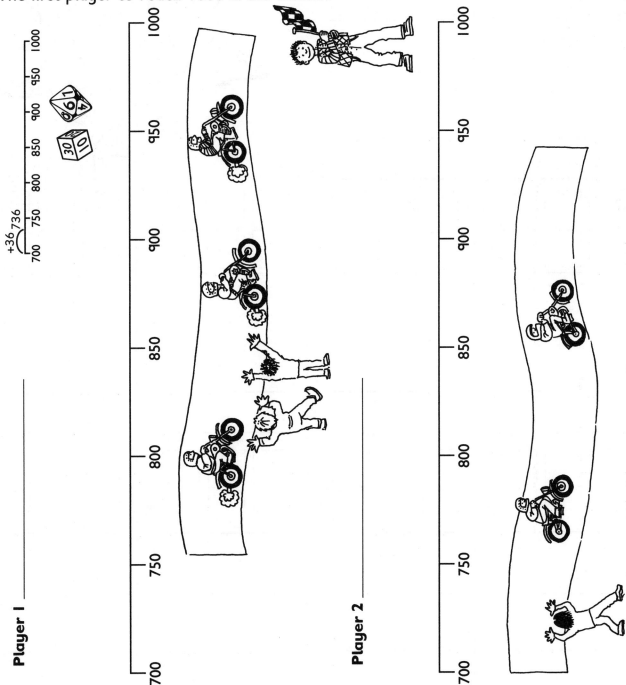

Player 1

Player 2

Name	Date

Roll the dice

You will need: three 0–9 dice

Instructions

● Roll three 0–9 dice.

● Using the three digits, make two different three-digit numbers.
Add them together.

6	2	5	
2	5	6	+
8	0	0	
	7	0	
	1	1	
8	8	1	

Name	Date

What was subtracted?

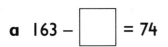

Work out the missing numbers from these subtraction calculations.
Use your own method. An empty number line may help you.

a $163 - \boxed{} = 74$

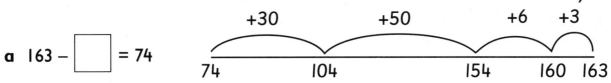

```
        +30           +50        +6   +3
   ⌢           ⌢          ⌢    ⌢
  74         104        154    160  163
```

b $152 - \boxed{} = 60$ _____

c $274 - \boxed{} = 186$ _____

d $368 - \boxed{} = 174$ _____

e $372 - \boxed{} = 183$ _____

f $416 - \boxed{} = 229$ _____

g $463 - \boxed{} = 167$ _____

h $581 - \boxed{} = 285$ _____

i $657 - \boxed{} = 267$ _____

j $783 - \boxed{} = 397$ _____

Collins Primary Maths © HarperCollins*Publishers* Ltd 2000

Name _____ Date _____

Handfuls of money

You will need: a box of coins

Take a handful of coins from the box. Count how much
money you have. Write the amount in pound and pence
in the table. Then write the amount in pence only.

Pounds and pence	Pence
£4·67	467p

Pounds and pence	Pence

Collins Primary Maths © HarperCollins*Publishers* Ltd 2000

Name _____   Date _____

Constructing spirals in millimetres

1   This spiral increases by 5 mm on each new side.

   a Continue the spiral as far as you can go.

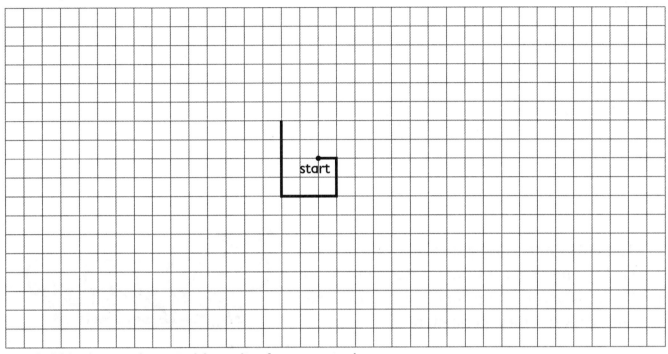

start

   b Work out the total length of your spiral.

   My spiral measures _____ cm altogether.

2   **a** Continue this spiral on the 5 mm triangular dotty paper as far as you can go.

start

   b My spiral measures _____ cm altogether.

Collins Primary Maths © HarperCollins*Publishers* Ltd 2000

Name _____   Date _____

Perimeter search

1 Draw 2 rectangles and 1 other shape with the
same perimeter as the square.

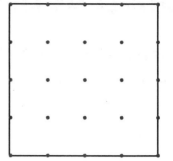

2 The dots on this grid paper are 1 cm apart.
Find the perimeter of these caterpillars in cm.

3 Draw different caterpillars in the space below
and work out their perimeters.

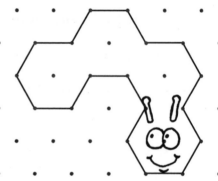

Collins Primary Maths © HarperCollins*Publishers* Ltd 2000

Name _____ Date _____

Co-ordinates connections

You can make (5, 2) or (2, 5) with this throw.

A game for 2 players

You will need: 2 dice in different colours or sizes, counters in two colours

Instructions

● Decide which die will represent the horizontal co-ordinate and which the vertical co-ordinate.

● On your turn, throw both dice and cover the co-ordinate with one of your counters.

● If a co-ordinate is already covered, you miss that turn.

● The winner is the first player to have three counters in a row, horizontal, vertical or diagonal.

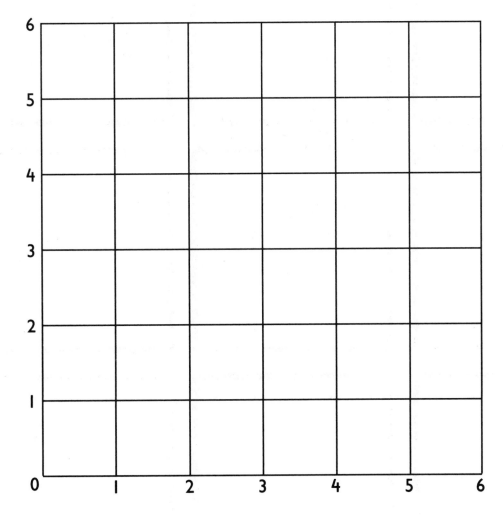

Variation

Throw both dice.

Decide which co-ordinate to make.

Collins Primary Maths © HarperCollinsPublishers Ltd 2000

Name _____ Date _____

Halving pinboard areas

Find different ways to halve the
area of each pinboard.
You can connect the pins with
vertical, horizontal or diagonal
lines.

Remember each
half must have the
same area.

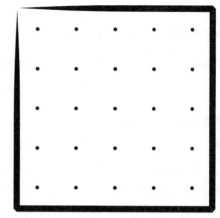

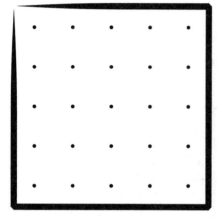

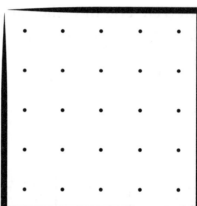

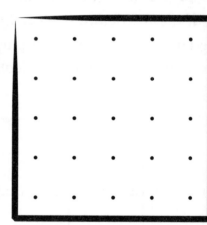

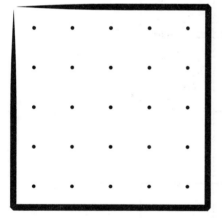

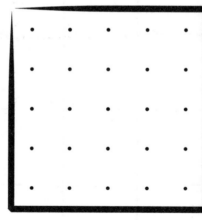

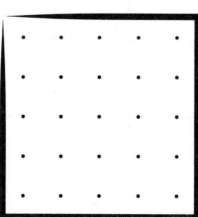

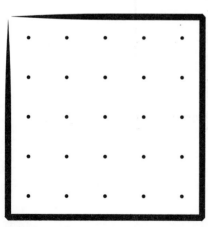

Collins Primary Maths © HarperCollinsPublishers Ltd 2000

Name	Date

Investigating L-shapes

1 Work out the area and perimeter of each L-shape.
Record your results in the table below.

Shape 1   Shape 2   Shape 3   Shape 4

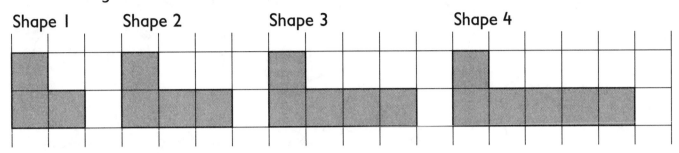

2 Draw the next two shapes in this grid.

Shape 5   Shape 6

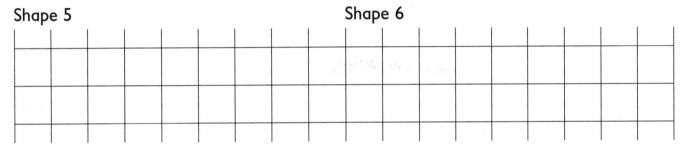

Write the answers in the table.

Number of shape	Area in cm²	Perimeter in cm
1	3 cm²	8 cm
2		
3		
4		
5		
6		
7		
8		
9		
10		

3 Work out the area and perimeter of the 10th shape and record it in the table.

4 Explain how you worked it out.

_____

Name _____ Date _____

All 4s

1 Complete each bracelet by following the rule in the middle. Start at the number shown.

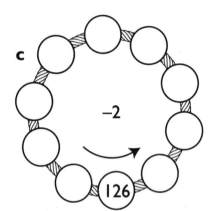

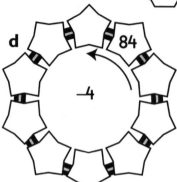

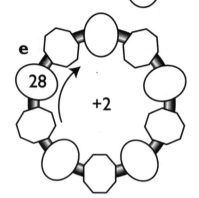

2 Fill in the numbers on the grid. Count in 4s from 0 and colour the numbers you land on.

1	2	3	4	5	6

a What do you notice?

_____

b If you went on, would 44 be in your sequence?

_____

c Would 52?

_____

d How do you know?

_____

3 Fill in the numbers on the grid starting at 2. Count on in 4s and colour the numbers you land on.

2	3	4	5	6	7

a What do you notice?

_____

b Is the pattern the same?

_____

c If you went on, would 44 be in your sequence?

_____

d How do you know?

_____

Name _____   Date _____

Adding multiples of 25

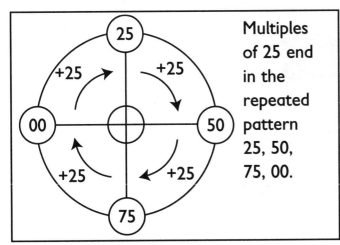

Multiples of 25 end in the repeated pattern 25, 50, 75, 00.

● Look at the cycle.
● Start anywhere on the cycle.
● Follow the arrows around the number of 25s you need.
● Your answer will always have one of the endings shown on the cycle. For example:
● Start at 25. Add 50 (2 lots of 25). Finish at 75.
● Start at 175. Add 75 (3 lots of 25). Finish at 250.

1   Complete the table using the cycle to help you.

Start	Add/subtract	Finish	Number sentence
75	+ 50	125	75 + 50 = 125
25	+ 2 lots of 25		
100	+ 75		
175	+ 25		
250	+ 3 lots of 25		
325	− 50		
475	+ 75		
300	− 25		
250	− 75		
	+ 50	325	
	− 25	450	
	− 75	225	
	+ 100	325	

2   Answer these:

a 75 + 50 = ☐   b 150 + 75 = ☐   c 225 + 100 = ☐

d 350 + 25 = ☐   e 425 + 75 = ☐   f 375 + 75 = ☐

g 500 − 75 = ☐   h 425 − 50 = ☐   i 350 − 25 = ☐

Name _____ Date _____

Know your division facts

A game for 2 or 3 players

You will need: 36 counters

Instruction

● Cover each division fact with a counter.

● Take turns to uncover a fact and give the answer.

● If the answer is correct, keep the counter.

● The player with the most counters at the end is the winner.

15 ÷ 3	28 ÷ 4	10 ÷ 10	40 ÷ 5	2 ÷ 2	32 ÷ 4
18 ÷ 3	16 ÷ 4	30 ÷ 10	24 ÷ 3	12 ÷ 2	40 ÷ 10
8 ÷ 4	24 ÷ 4	5 ÷ 1	35 ÷ 5	9 ÷ 3	70 ÷ 10
50 ÷ 5	8 ÷ 2	18 ÷ 2	4 ÷ 4	21 ÷ 3	12 ÷ 4
12 ÷ 3	27 ÷ 3	16 ÷ 2	45 ÷ 9	60 ÷ 10	3 ÷ 3
25 ÷ 5	5 ÷ 5	30 ÷ 5	14 ÷ 2	36 ÷ 4	20 ÷ 4

Collins Primary Maths © HarperCollinsPublishers Ltd 2000

Name _____　　Date _____

Recording division calculations

Use the method shown to find the answer to each division calculation.
Approximate the answer first. Write your approximation on the notepad.

a　$58 \div 2 =$ ☐ 29
$$\begin{array}{r} 58 \\ -40 \quad 20 \times 2 \\ \hline 18 \\ -18 \quad 9 \times 2 \\ \hline 0 \end{array}$$
$60 \div 2$
$= 30$

b　$70 \div 5 =$ ☐

c　$76 \div 4 =$ ☐

d　$96 \div 3 =$ ☐

e　$94 \div 2 =$ ☐

f　$69 \div 3 =$ ☐

g　$87 \div 3 =$ ☐

h　$75 \div 5 =$ ☐

i　$52 \div 4 =$ ☐

j　$48 \div 3 =$ ☐

k　$54 \div 2 =$ ☐

l　$90 \div 2 =$ ☐

m　$68 \div 4 =$ ☐

n　$56 \div 4 =$ ☐

Collins Primary Maths © HarperCollins*Publishers* Ltd 2000

Name _____ Date _____

Fast 5s

Play the game Fast 5s – it's like noughts and crosses!

A game for 2 players

You will need: a set of coloured counters each

Instruction

● Take turns to choose 1 number from the labels on the left.

● Multiply the number by 5 the quick way.

● If your answer is on the grid, place one of your counters on that square.

● The winner is the first person to get 3 in a row, column or diagonal.

Remember the quick way to ×5.

first ×10
then ÷2

Game 1

15	20	18	26
22	13	40	28
14	11	25	50

100	55	90
250	65	110
200	70	130

Game 2

12	20	50	17
19	16	30	45
25	18	40	35

80	225	95
200	150	125
250	90	60

Collins Primary Maths © HarperCollins*Publishers* Ltd 2000

Name		Date

Finding quarters

1 Find one quarter of each number by halving and then halving again.

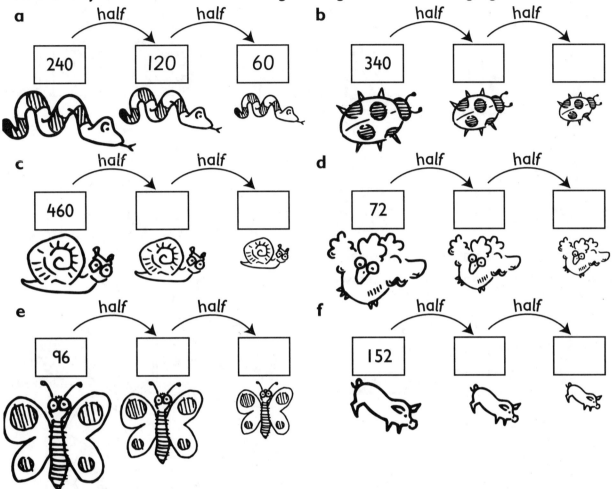

a
half → half →
240 → 120 → 60

b
half → half →
340 → ☐ → ☐

c
half → half →
460 → ☐ → ☐

d
half → half →
72 → ☐ → ☐

e
half → half →
96 → ☐ → ☐

f
half → half →
152 → ☐ → ☐

2 Complete each number web. Find one quarter
of the number shown by halving and then halving again.

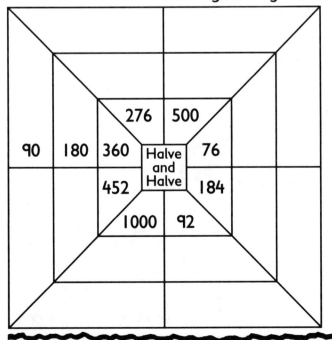

276 500
90 180 360 Halve and Halve 76
452 184
1000 92

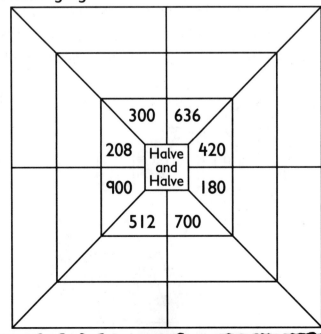

300 636
208 Halve and Halve 420
900 180
512 700

Collins Primary Maths © HarperCollinsPublishers Ltd 2000

● Begin to relate fractions to division and find simple fractions such as $\frac{1}{2}$, $\frac{1}{3}$, $\frac{1}{4}$ of numbers

ECM 18

Name _____ Date _____

Fraction bashers

1 Calculate the numbers that come out of the machines.

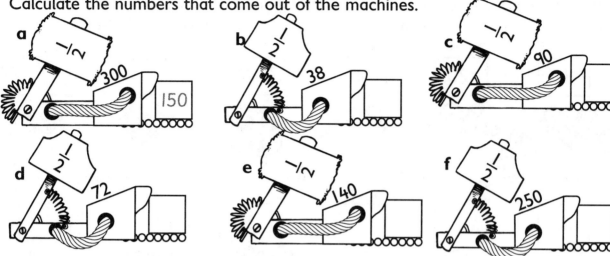

a $\frac{1}{2}$ 300 150

b $\frac{1}{2}$ 38

c $\frac{1}{2}$ 90

d $\frac{1}{2}$ 72

e $\frac{1}{2}$ 140

f $\frac{1}{2}$ 250

2 The first machine halves the number.
The second machine halves the answer.

a $\frac{1}{2}$ 32 $\frac{1}{2}$ 16 8

b $\frac{1}{2}$ 60 $\frac{1}{2}$

c $\frac{1}{2}$ 56 $\frac{1}{2}$

d $\frac{1}{2}$ 68 $\frac{1}{2}$

3 Calculate the numbers that come out of the machines.
The first machine finds a quarter of the number.
The second machine finds a quarter of the answer.

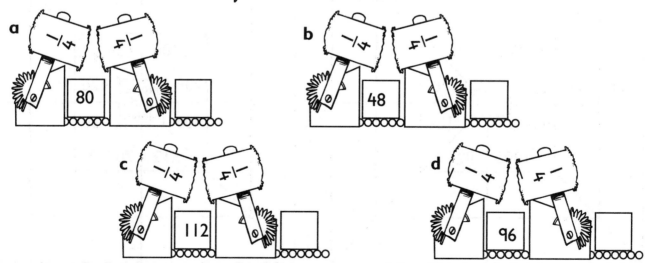

a $\frac{1}{4}$ 80 $\frac{1}{4}$

b $\frac{1}{4}$ 48 $\frac{1}{4}$

c $\frac{1}{4}$ 112 $\frac{1}{4}$

d $\frac{1}{4}$ 96 $\frac{1}{4}$

Collins Primary Maths © HarperCollins*Publishers* Ltd 2000

Name _____ Date _____

Billboard fractions

1 Write the missing fraction.

a 8 is $\frac{1}{5}$ of 40

b 5 is ____ of 40

c 4 is ____ of 24

d 3 is ____ of 27

e 20 is ____ of 120

f 5 is ____ of 35

g 70 is ____ of 140

h 9 is ____ of 10

i 10 is ____ of 200

j 6 is ____ of 36

2 What fraction of the larger measure is the smaller measure?

a

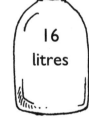
2 litres   16 litres

b

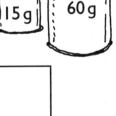
15g   60g

c
47g   94g

d
200 ml   600 ml

e
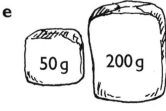

50 g   200 g

f
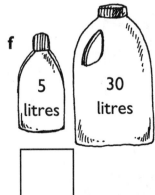
5 litres   30 litres

Name _____ Date _____

Adding three numbers

Add the three numbers together.
Write the calculation out vertically
then work out the answer.

Remember
to add the
units first!

a 153 + 62 + 71

b 264 + 84 + 39

c 381 + 77 + 65

d 463 + 92 + 56

e 547 + 163 + 58

f 412 + 295 + 67

g 387 + 359 + 76

h 478 + 319 + 82

i 156 + 298 + 374

j 423 + 191 + 241

a

	1	5	3	
		6	2	+
		7	1	
			6	
	1	8	0	
	1	0	0	
	2	8	6	

Collins Primary Maths © HarperCollins*Publishers* Ltd 2000

Name _____ Date _____

Puzzle time

1 Draw two straight lines across the analogue clock face so that the numbers in each section total 26.

_____

2 In two hours' time it will be as long after midnight as it is before noon. What time is it now?

midnight | 1 2 3 4 5 6 7 8 9 10 11 | noon

_____

3 Jacqui saw this clock face in a mirror. What time was it?

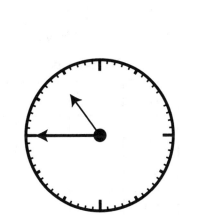

_____

4 You are an apprentice chef at the Royal Palace. You get this Royal order for breakfast.
There are no clocks or watches in the Royal kitchen. You find two egg-timers, one for 3 minutes and one for 5 minutes. Show how you will use them to time the eggs correctly.

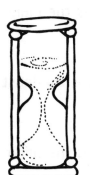

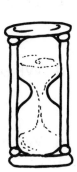

Boil two eggs.
King: hard-boiled for 7 minutes
Queen: soft-boiled for 4 minutes.
Both eggs must be ready at exactly the same time.

_____

_____

_____

Collins Primary Maths © HarperCollins*Publishers* Ltd 2000

Name _____ Date _____

Vowel pair pictograms

1 These words have pairs of vowels.

deep   pool   round   leak   piece

2 Find words with these vowel pairs in a reading book. Stop when one pair of vowels has a frequency of between 25 and 30. Make a tally mark for each word.

Vowel pair	Tally	Frequency
ee		
oo		
ou		
ea		
ie		

3 Count the tally marks.

Vowel pairs in words

4 Complete the pictogram. Choose your own picture to represent five words.

ee							
oo							
ou							
ea							
ie							

Number of words

5 Now answer these questions.

   a How many words had the vowel pair **ou**?

   _____

   b What is the frequency for **ee**?

   _____

   c What is the highest frequency?

   _____

   d Which is the least frequent vowel pair?

   _____

   e What is the difference between the highest and lowest frequencies?

   _____

Key

Name _____ Date _____

In the middle

Speech bubbles:
- 250 is less than 300
- 100 is less than 250
- 250 is in between 100 and 300

$100 < 250 <$

$< 250 < 300$

$100 < 250 < 300$

1 Write your own number in the box.

a 270 < ☐ < 2700   **b** 4209 < ☐ < 4215   **c** 1999 < ☐ < 2100

d 1905 < ☐ < 1950   **e** 5990 < ☐ < 6000   **f** 9999 < ☐ < 10003

2 Put these numbers in the boxes.

a 6927	**b** 4929	**c** 2101
5850	2499	2011
5842	4994	2110

☐ < ☐ < ☐   ☐ < ☐ < ☐   ☐ < ☐ < ☐

3 Write your own numbers in the boxes.

a 74 > ☐ > 43   **b** 9817 > ☐ > 891   **c** 2300 > ☐ > 2294

d 8020 > ☐ > 8009   **e** 1909 > ☐ > 1099   **f** 782 > ☐ > 728

4 Put the numbers in the boxes.

a 693	**b** 4099	**c** 7077
369	4909	7770
396	4109	7007

☐ > ☐ > ☐   ☐ > ☐ > ☐   ☐ > ☐ > ☐

Collins Primary Maths © HarperCollinsPublishers Ltd 2000

Name _____ Date _____

Roll the number

1 Which number is missing from each calculation?

a 60 + ◯ + 30 = 120   m ◯ + 60 + 90 = 200

b 70 + 50 + ◯ = 180   n 60 + 60 + ◯ = 210

c 80 + ◯ + 60 = 140   o 70 + 50 + ◯ = 200

d ◯ + 40 + 70 = 150   p 60 + ◯ + 90 = 240

e ◯ + 30 + 90 = 170   q 80 + 80 + ◯ = 250

f 40 + 50 + ◯ = 120   r 70 + ◯ + 90 = 240

g 70 + ◯ + 60 = 170   s 30 + ◯ + 80 = 200

h 10 + 80 + ◯ = 140   t 70 + 60 + ◯ = 210

i 50 + ◯ + 70 = 180   u 80 + ◯ + 90 = 220

j ◯ + 90 + 40 = 190   v 70 + 70 + ◯ = 210

k 20 + 80 + ◯ = 160   w 80 + 60 + ◯ = 220

l 70 + ◯ + 50 = 130   x 90 + ◯ + 70 = 230

Collins Primary Maths © HarperCollins*Publishers* Ltd 2000

| Name _____ | Date _____ |

Adding vertically

Write out these calculations vertically and then work out the answers.
Remember to write the digits in the correct column.

a 624 + 75 =

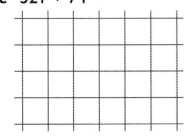

b 416 + 82 =

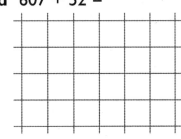

c 521 + 74 =

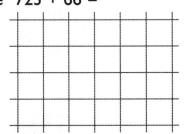

d 607 + 52 =

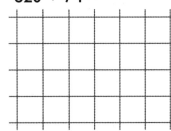

e 723 + 66 =

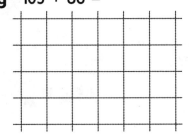

f 820 + 79 =

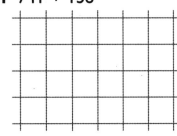

g 903 + 86 =

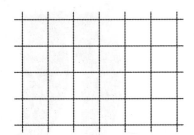

h 741 + 158 =

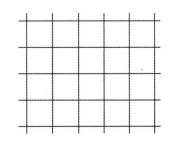

i 513 + 274 =

j 320 + 463 =

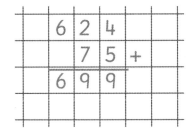
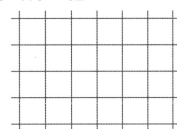

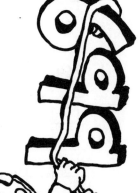

Collins Primary Maths © HarperCollins*Publishers* Ltd 2000

Name _____ Date _____

The answer is ...

Work out the calculations. In some of them
the ten and the units digit need changing.

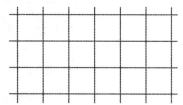

	3	2	
4	³8	⁵5	
1	5	8	−
2	7	7	

a 648 − 372 =   **b** 567 − 294 =

c 453 − 128 =   **d** 783 − 559 =

e 328 − 165 =   **f** 829 − 477 =

g 817 − 367 =   **h** 761 − 585 =

These calculations need the tens and the units digit changing.

i 764 − 296 =   **j** 852 − 374 =

k 926 − 387 =   **l** 658 − 269 =

Collins Primary Maths © HarperCollins*Publishers* Ltd 2000

Name	Date

How much?

1 Help these children to work out how much they have spent.

   a £4·63 + £3·49 =

   b £5·99 + £2·26 =

   c £3·96 + £2·45 =

   d £6·56 + £2·76 =

   e £8·77 + £1·69 =

£4·63
£3·49 +
£8·12

2 Help these children to work out how much they
will have left after they have bought something.

   a £8·23 − £5·46 =

   b £7·52 − £1·75 =

   c £9·41 − £4·76 =

   d £5·54 − £2·78 =

   e £8·28 − £5·39 =

Collins Primary Maths © HarperCollins*Publishers* Ltd 2000

Name	Date

Routes to the game

How many different routes can Simon take from his hotel to the baseball park if he can travel only south-west or south-east? Record each route on a different grid. There are some extra grids if you need them.

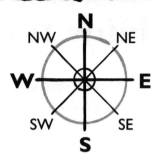

a
Hotel

Park
<u>ISW, 2SE, ISW</u>

b
Hotel

Park

c
Hotel

Park

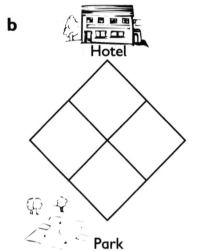

d
Hotel

Park

e
Hotel

Park

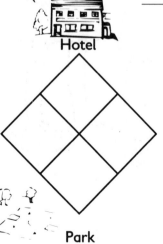

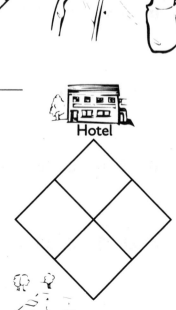

f
Hotel

Park

g
Hotel

Park

h
Hotel

Park

Collins Primary Maths © HarperCollins*Publishers* Ltd 2000

Name _____ Date _____

Investigating set square angles

Here are three ways of fitting together the angles of two set squares.

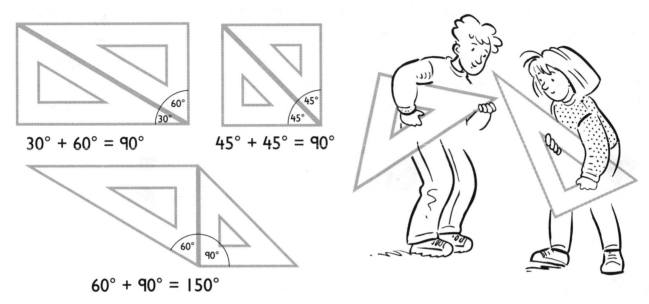

30° + 60° = 90°   45° + 45° = 90°

60° + 90° = 150°

1 How many different ways can you fit together two set square
angles to make these angles? Record your answers in this table.

Degrees	2 set square angles	Degrees	2 set square angles
60°	30° + 30°	75°	
90°		105°	
120°		135°	
150°		180°	

2 How many different ways can you make these angles by fitting
together three set squares? Record your answers in this table.

Degrees	3 set square angles
90°	
105°	
120°	
135°	
150°	
165°	
180°	

Collins Primary Maths © HarperCollinsPublishers Ltd 2000

Name _____   Date _____

Nets for a mouse

1   Carefully cut out all three shapes along the black lines.

2   Using a ruler, score carefully along the dotted lines.

3   Fold up the faces and stick down the tabs to make a large (body) and small (head) tetrahedron.

4   Fold the rectangle in half along the line of dashes.

5   Stick together the faces marked A, then the faces marked B.

You need:
● scissors
● ruler
● glue or sticky tape

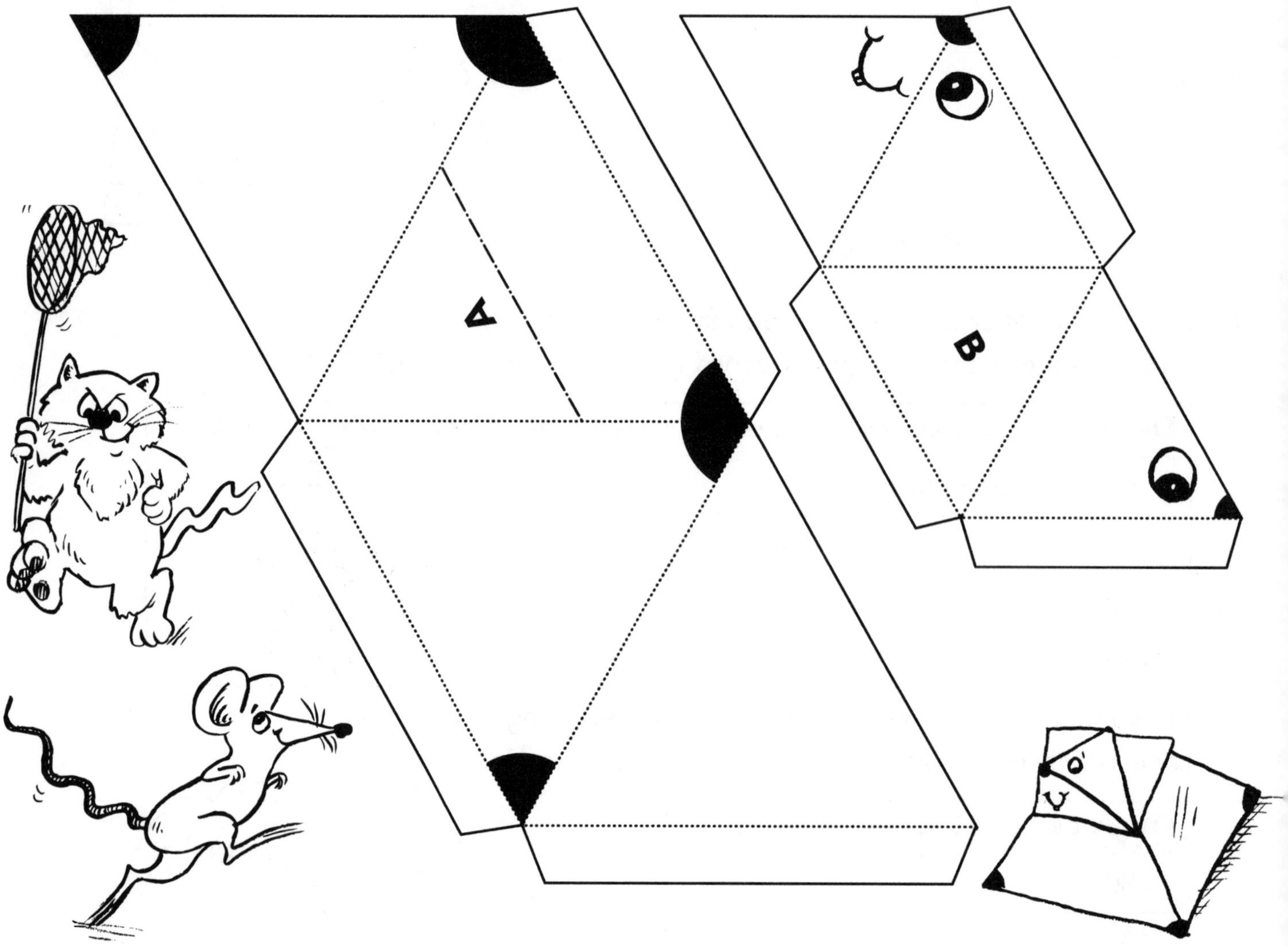

A

B

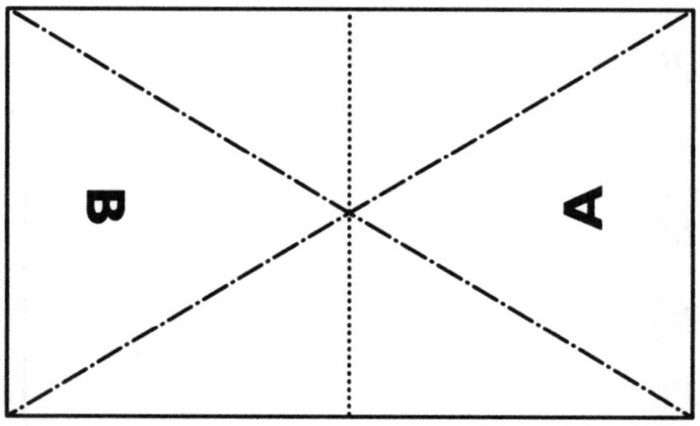

cut ——————

score and fold ·············

position —·—·—·—·—

B   A

Name _____ Date _____

Folding a regular pentagon

1 Fold a sheet of A4 paper from corner to corner to make this shape.

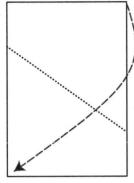  

2 Turn the shape round…   …fold it in half and open it out.

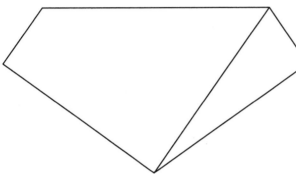

3 Fold these edges to meet at the centre line and turn the shape over.

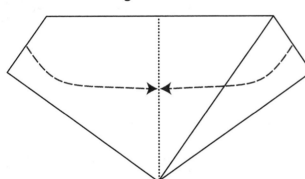 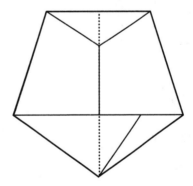

4 Now half and quarter another sheet of A4 coloured paper.

A5
A6   A6

5 Work with a friend to make pentagons like these.

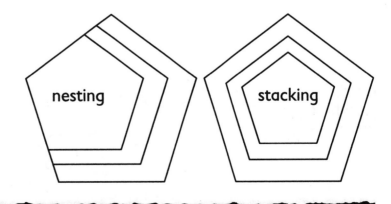

nesting   stacking

Collins Primary Maths © HarperCollinsPublishers Ltd 2000

Name _____   Date _____

Counting forwards and backwards

1 Throw the number die to find how many to jump each time. Write the number in the box.

2 Start at the number in the first circle.

3 Throw the operation die each time. Add or subtract the number in the box. Write the new number.

You need:
- a blank die, marked 3, 4, 5, 3, 4, 5
- a blank die, marked +, −, +, −, +, −

a

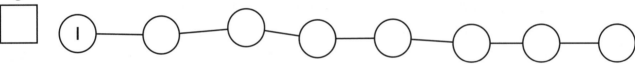

b

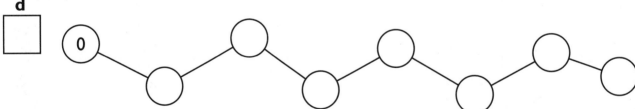

c

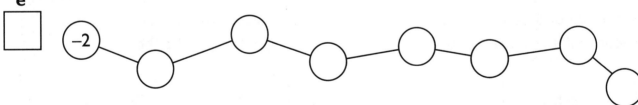

d

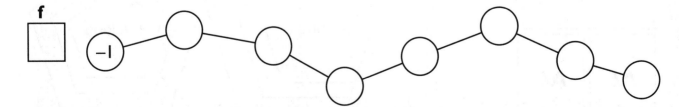

e

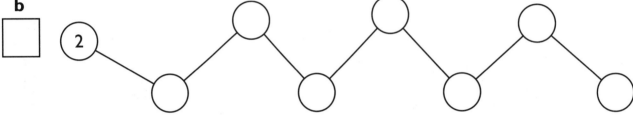

f

Name _____   Date _____

Counting in 25s game

Instructions   (For 2 players)

1 Start at 0.
2 Take turns to throw the die.
3 Move your playing piece forwards or backwards 25 or 50 as shown on the dice.
4 The winner is the first person to reach 300 exactly.

You need:
● 2 playing pieces
● a blank die, marked +25, −25, +50, −50, 0, 0

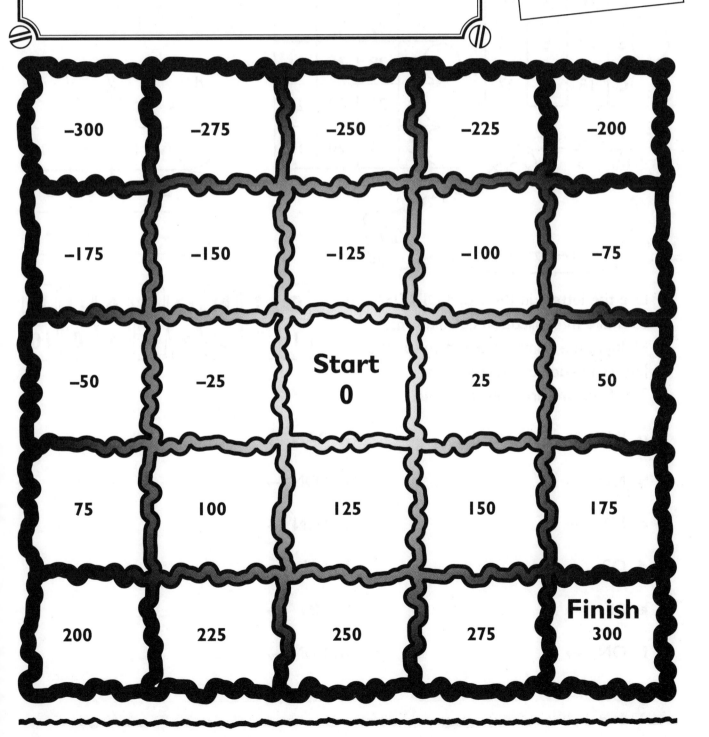

−300	−275	−250	−225	−200
−175	−150	−125	−100	−75
−50	−25	**Start 0**	25	50
75	100	125	150	175
200	225	250	275	**Finish 300**

Collins Primary Maths © HarperCollins*Publishers* Ltd 2000

Name _____ Date _____

Revising multiplication and division facts

1 Find the value of each of the letters in these puzzles.
Write it in the circle by each letter.

a

×	D	E	F
5 A	30	10	45
B	24	8	36
C	18	6	27

b

×	D	E	F
A	28	35	21
B	32	40	24
C	16	20	12

c

÷	D	E	F
A	6	12	18
B	4	8	12
C	3	6	9

d

÷	D	E	F
A	10	15	20
B	4	6	8
C	2	3	4

2 Use the letters in the word DINOSAUR
to make multiplication calculations.
Multiply the numbers standing for the
letters in each of these words.
The first two are done for you.

D	I	N	O	S	A	U	R
1	2	3	4	5	6	8	10

a IN → $2 \times 3 = 6$

b NO → _____

c SO → _____

d OR → _____

e AS → _____

f ON → _____

g IS → _____

h RAN → $\quad 10 \times (6 \times 3) = 10 \times 18$
$\qquad\qquad = 180$

i SON → _____

j SUN → _____

k SAD → _____

l SIN → _____

m RUN → _____

n RID → _____

Collins Primary Maths © HarperCollins*Publishers* Ltd 2000

Name _____ Date _____

Writing word problems

Use the pictures below to help you write your own division problems.

● You may use each picture more than once.

● Write problems that involve dividing by 2, 3, 4, 5, or 10.

● Calculate the answers to your problems.

Write your problems here.

a	b
Answer: _____	Answer: _____
c	**d**
Answer: _____	Answer: _____
e	**f**
Answer: _____	Answer: _____
g	**h**
Answer: _____	Answer: _____

Collins Primary Maths © HarperCollins*Publishers* Ltd 2000

Name _____ Date _____

Easy elevens

Play the game Easy elevens (it's like noughts and crosses).

Instructions (For 2 players)
- One player uses one colour of counters, the other uses the other colour.
- Choose one number from the labels on the left.
- Multiply the number by 11 the quick way.
- If your answer is on the grid, put your counter on that square.
- The winner is the first person to get 3 counters in a row.

You need:
- 2 piles of counters, in two different colours

To multiply by 11 ... Think: multiply by 10 then add the number you are multiplying 11 by.

Game 1

15	12	18
20	26	11
5	23	30
25	13	8

286	121	220
55	165	143
198	330	275

Game 2

9	14	19
22	27	16
12	10	17
21	24	29

209	176	319
297	231	110
264	154	242

Collins Primary Maths © HarperCollins*Publishers* Ltd 2000

Name _____ Date _____

Recording multiplication

The table shows how many balloons were sold over one week.

Number of balloons per pack	Monday	Tuesday	Wednesday	Thursday	Friday
Red 3	24	64	36	45	81
Blue 4	72	46	24	36	43
Yellow 5	35	66	49	18	38
Green 6	26	43	72	35	19

I Use the table to help answer the questions. Approximate your
answer first in the thought bubble.

a Red balloons are sold in packs of 3.
How many red balloons were sold
altogether on Tuesday?

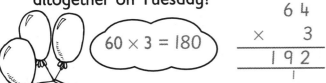

$60 \times 3 = 180$

$$\begin{array}{r} 6\,4 \\ \times \quad 3 \\ \hline 1\,9\,2 \\ {\scriptstyle 1} \end{array}$$

b Blue balloons are sold in packs of 4.
How many blue balloons were sold
on Thursday?

_____

c Yellow balloons are sold in packs of 5.
How many yellow balloons were sold
on Friday?

_____

d Green balloons are sold in packs of 6.
How many green balloons were sold
altogether on Wednesday?

_____

e How many blue balloons were sold
altogether on Monday?

_____

f How many yellow balloons were sold
altogether on Monday?

_____

g How many green balloons were sold
altogether on Tuesday?

_____

h How many red balloons were sold
altogether on Thursday?

_____

Name _____   Date _____

Bottled fractions

1 Write two fractions to show the opened bottles.

a

$$\frac{4}{8} = \frac{1}{2}$$

b

_____

c

_____

d

_____

e

_____

f

_____

2 Write two fractions to show the opened bottles.

a

_____

b

_____

c

_____

d

_____

e

_____

f

_____

3 Complete the table.

$\frac{1}{2} = \frac{}{4}$	$\frac{1}{3} = \frac{}{6}$	$\frac{1}{4} = \frac{}{8}$	$\frac{1}{5} = \frac{}{10}$
$\frac{1}{2} = \frac{3}{6}$	$\frac{2}{3} = \frac{}{6}$	$\frac{2}{4} = \frac{}{8}$	$\frac{2}{5} = \frac{}{10}$
$\frac{1}{2} = \frac{}{8}$		$\frac{3}{4} = \frac{}{8}$	$\frac{3}{5} = \frac{}{10}$
$\frac{1}{2} = \frac{}{10}$			$\frac{4}{5} = \frac{}{10}$

Collins Primary Maths © HarperCollins*Publishers* Ltd 2000

Name _____ Date _____

Decimal problems

1 Add the prices together.
Change them to pence first.

a 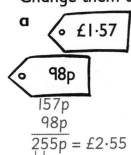 £1·57

98p

$$\begin{array}{r} 157p \\ 98p \\ \hline 255p = £2·55 \\ \tiny 1\ 1 \end{array}$$

b £1·62

85p

c 97p

29p

d £5·83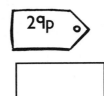

£2·65

2 The cup is more expensive. How much more?

a 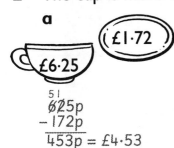 £1·72

£6·25

$$\begin{array}{r} \tiny 5\ 1 \\ 6\!\!\!/2\!\!\!/5p \\ -172p \\ \hline 453p = £4·53 \end{array}$$

b £1·38

£4·69

c £3·47

£5·00

d 75p

£9·41

3 Calculate the total length of rope.
Change the lengths to centimetres first.

a 5·63 m

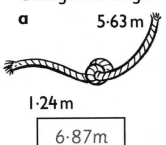

1·24 m

| 6·87m |

b 4·29 m

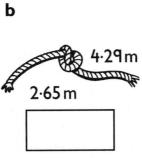

2·65 m

c 1·65 m

52 cm

d 39 cm

95 cm

4 Linda cut some hose pipe from a reel.
How much is left on the reel?

a

6·94 m

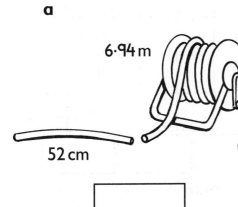

52 cm

b

5·60 m

3·48 m

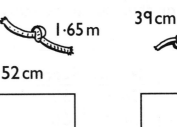

c

9·08 m

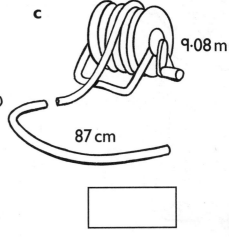

87 cm

Collins Primary Maths © HarperCollinsPublishers Ltd 2000

Name	Date

Estimating bar charts

1 The bar chart shows children's scores in a game.
Estimate their scores and write them in the table.

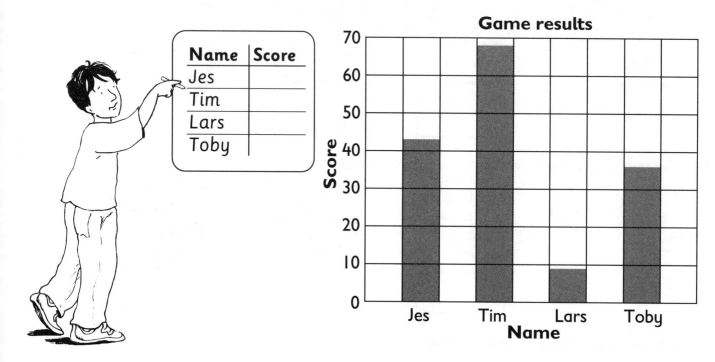

Name	Score
Jes	
Tim	
Lars	
Toby	

Game results

2 Draw a bar chart for these scores.

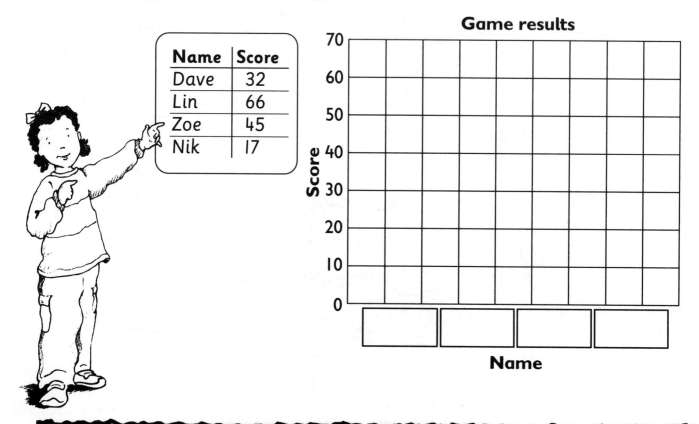

Name	Score
Dave	32
Lin	66
Zoe	45
Nik	17

Game results

Name _____ Date _____

Calculate and order

Calculate each answer.

Order your answers, smallest to largest.

1

a	$95 \div 10$	27×10	$430 \div 10$	order		9·5	43	270
b	4×10	$480 \div 10$	$460 \div 10$	order				
c	285×10	$2580 \div 10$	208×10	order				
d	$10\,000 \div 10$	999×10	9090×10	order				

2

a	2×95	20×40	2×350	order				
b	20×16	2×130	20×12	order				
c	20×23	2×24	20×22	order				
d	2×380	20×36	2×330	order				

3

a	27×10	3×100	20×100	order				
b	95×100	$9050 \div 10$	590×10	order				
c	$36\,900 \div 10$	36×100	396×10	order				
d	800×10	88×100	$80\,800 \div 10$	order				

4

a	2×74	$3520 \div 10$	28×10	order				
b	20×21	4×100	$4300 \div 10$	order				
c	$9000 \div 10$	20×46	10×91	order				
d	$20\,000 \div 10$	100×23	10×221	order				

Collins Primary Maths © HarperCollinsPublishers Ltd 2000

Name _____ Date _____

Find the missing multiple

a   90 + ☐ = 130

b   800 + ☐ = 1300

c   ☐ − 50 = 80

d   ☐ − 600 = 900

e   90 + ☐ = 150

f   ☐ − 400 = 700

g   ☐ + 80 = 170

h   500 + ☐ = 1400

i   ☐ − 50 = 70

j   1600 − ☐ = 800

k   ☐ + 90 = 170

l   500 + ☐ = 1200

m   60 + ☐ = 160

n   700 + ☐ = 1400

o   ☐ − 50 = 90

p   1500 − ☐ = 800

q   80 + ☐ = 160

r   ☐ − 400 = 900

s   ☐ − 20 = 90

t   800 + ☐ = 1600

2   Choose an addition calculation and explain in words
    how you worked out the answer.

_____

_____

3   Choose a subtraction calculation and explain in words
    how you worked out the answer.

_____

_____

Collins Primary Maths © HarperCollinsPublishers Ltd 2000

● Use known number facts and place value to add or subtract mentally

Name _____ Date _____

Complete the calculations

Work out the missing numbers.

a 38 + ☐ = 87

b 64 + ☐ = 102

c ☐ + 67 = 140

d 89 + ☐ = 163

e ☐ + 53 = 151

f ☐ + 68 = 137

g 82 + ☐ = 149

h 57 + ☐ = 119

i ☐ − 43 = 53

j 82 − ☐ = 17

k ☐ − 39 = 28

l 73 − ☐ = 19

m ☐ − 47 = 34

n ☐ − 38 = 51

o 73 − ☐ = 47

p 97 − ☐ = 13

q 87 + ☐ = 116

r ☐ + 49 = 119

s ☐ − 59 = 25

t 88 − ☐ = 57

Collins Primary Maths © HarperCollins*Publishers* Ltd 2000

Name _____　　Date _____

Adding three numbers

Add three numbers together using the standard vertical method.

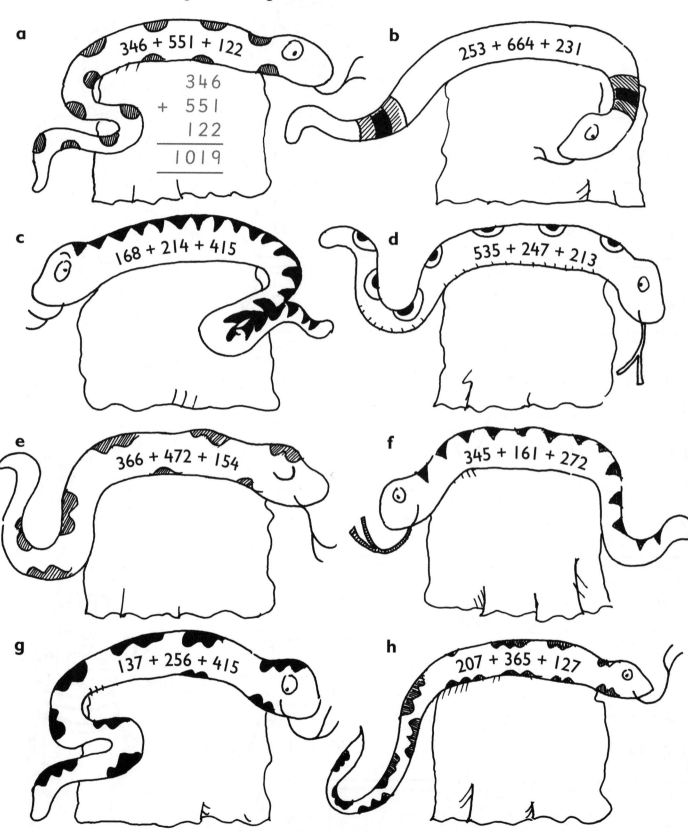

a   346 + 551 + 122

```
    346
  + 551
    122
  ‾‾‾‾‾
   1019
```

b   253 + 664 + 231

c   168 + 214 + 415

d   535 + 247 + 213

e   366 + 472 + 154

f   345 + 161 + 272

g   137 + 256 + 415

h   207 + 365 + 127

Collins Primary Maths © HarperCollinsPublishers Ltd 2000

Name _____   Date _____

Solving problems

Read the information and make up some questions to answer.

a   Jane made 67 sandwiches for the party.
She had wanted to make 100 but she ran
out of bread. Luckily Louise brought along
76 sandwiches with her. At the end of the
party 48 sandwiches were left over.

_____

_____

_____

_____

b   1200 people watched the football match between
the reds and the blues. 500 of them supported
the red team. It started to rain at half time
and 900 fans were left. Then 6 fans had to
leave early to get their train home. 621 blue
fans saw their team win at the end of the match.

_____

_____

_____

_____

c   581 children walked into assembly. 293 of
them were from the infants. The head teacher
sent out 9 children for talking. 27 children
from class 4 had to leave before the end as
they were going on a trip. At the end of the
assembly 254 junior children were left.

_____

_____

_____

_____

Collins Primary Maths © HarperCollins*Publishers* Ltd 2000

Name _____   Date _____

Measuring cylinders

When these measuring cylinders are filled with water, they will hold 1000 ml or 1 litre. Complete the labels to show how full or empty each cylinder is when the water reaches the level shown by the arrow.

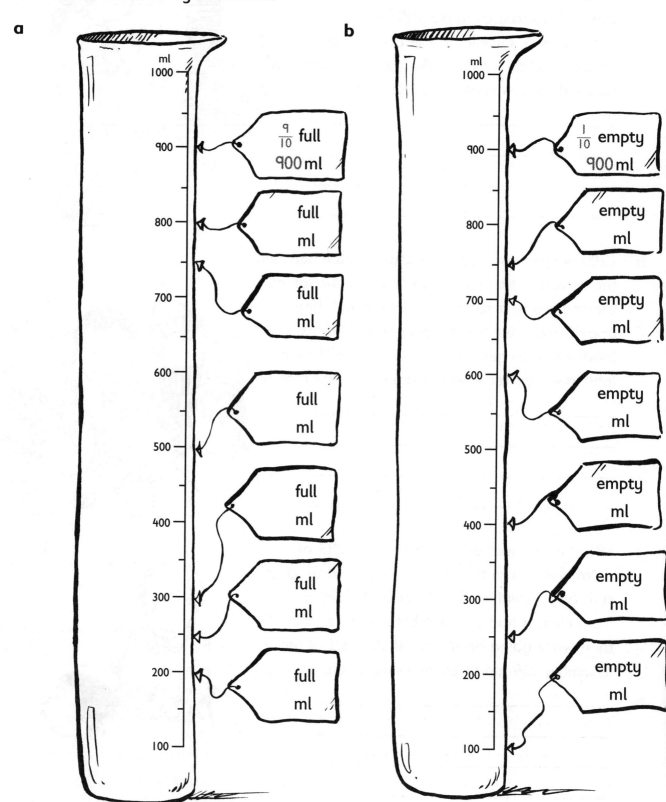

a

$\frac{9}{10}$ full
900 ml

full
ml

full
ml

full
ml

full
ml

full
ml

full
ml

b

$\frac{1}{10}$ empty
900 ml

empty
ml

empty
ml

empty
ml

empty
ml

empty
ml

empty
ml

Collins Primary Maths © HarperCollins*Publishers* Ltd 2000

Name	Date

Measuring displacement

Work with a partner.

You will need: a measuring jar,
coloured water, about 60 interlocking 1 cm cubes

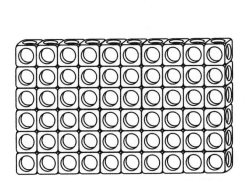
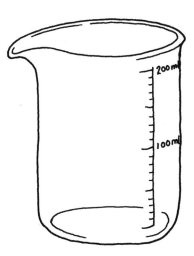

1   Pour coloured water into a measuring jar to the 100 ml mark.

2   Make a cuboid with 20 cubes and drop it into the water. Make sure the cuboid is submerged.

3   Record the new water level to the nearest 10 ml, in the table below.

4   Use all 20 cubes and make a different cuboid.

Measure the level the water rose to the nearest 10 ml and record.

Make sure that all of the cuboid is under the water.

5

a water level at start	100ml	100ml	100ml	100ml	100ml	100ml
b number of cubes in cuboid	20	20	30	40	50	60
c level to which water rose	ml	ml	ml	ml	ml	ml
d difference between a and c						

6   Repeat step 2 using 30 cubes and record your results in the table.

7   Estimate, then measure the new water levels for 40, 50 and 60 cubes.

8   **a** Write what you notice about your results.

    b Can you predict by how much the water will rise if 100 cubes are added?

_____

_____

Name _____ Date _____

Reflecting shapes

1   Draw the reflection of each half shape.

a

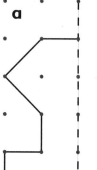

b

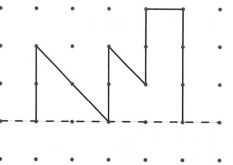

c

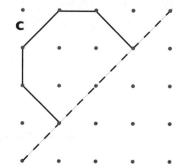

e

d

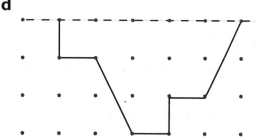

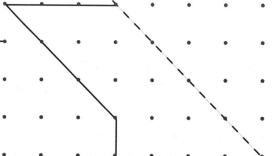

2   Colour some of the triangles in each half shape.
    Reflect the half shape in a mirror then complete each shape.

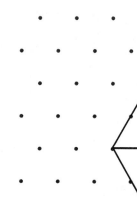

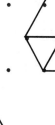

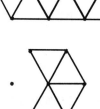

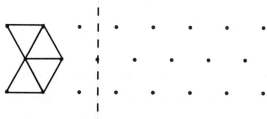

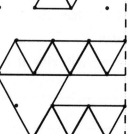

Collins Primary Maths © HarperCollins*Publishers* Ltd 2000

ECM . 48

| Name _____ | Date _____ |

Stained glass fanlights

The windows in the hall of Oakwood Primary School
are fan-shaped and have 4 panes of glass.
The glass is fitted in the school
colours of blue and gold.

1 How many different ways can the panes of glass be fitted?
Use the diagrams to help you.

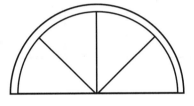   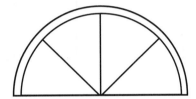   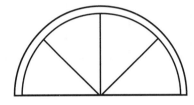

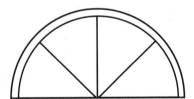   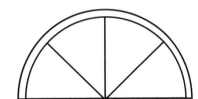   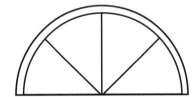

2 What if the school colours are blue, gold and brown?
How many different ways can you fit the glass if two of the panes are blue?

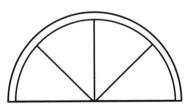   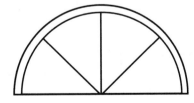   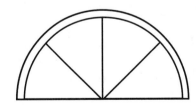

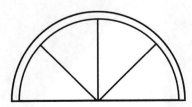   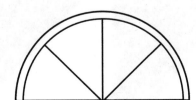   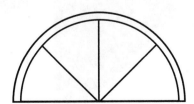

3 What if two of the panes are gold or brown?
Use the back of the sheet.

Collins Primary Maths © HarperCollins*Publishers* Ltd 2000

Name _____   Date _____

New patterns from old

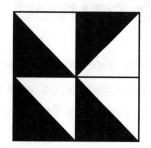

Cut out the 4 squares at the foot of the page.

1   Make a large square with your 4 squares, like this.

2   Now make as many different patterns as you can.

3   If you need more grids, use the reverse of this sheet.

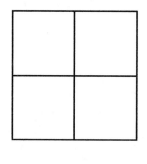
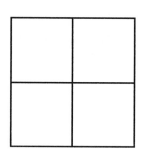
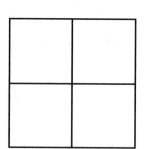
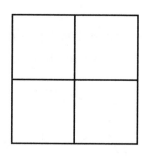

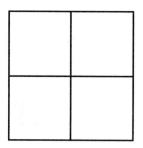
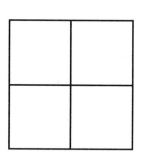
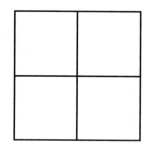
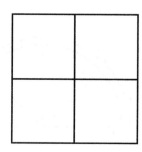

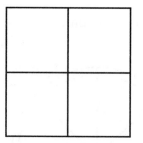
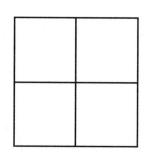
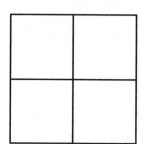
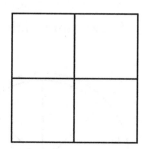

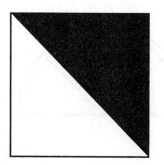
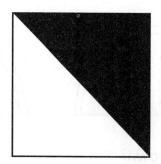
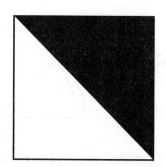
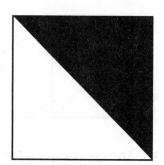

Collins Primary Maths © HarperCollins*Publishers* Ltd 2000

Name _____   Date _____

Sorting multiples of 2, 3, 4, 5, and 10

Sort the numbers into the correct box.
Use the "multiples of" labels to help you.
Some numbers may go into more than one box.

a

9 99 45 44 36 16 24 12 39 27

Multiples of 2   Multiples of 3

b

36 55 84 20 32 40 16 100 125 56

Multiples of 4   Multiples of 5

c

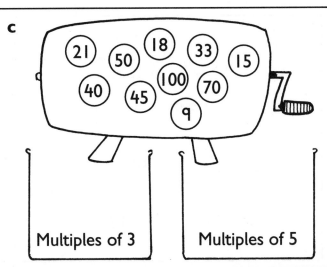

21 50 18 33 40 45 100 70 15 9

Multiples of 3   Multiples of 5

d

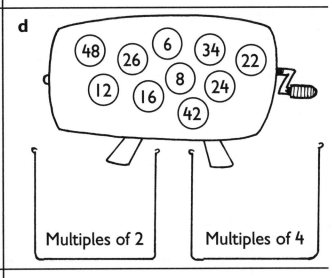

48 26 6 34 12 16 8 24 22 42

Multiples of 2   Multiples of 4

e

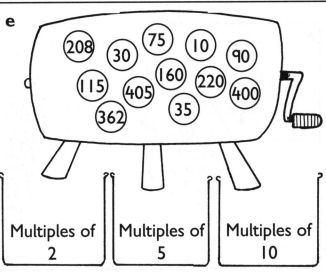

208 30 75 10 90 115 405 160 220 400 362 35

Multiples of 2   Multiples of 5   Multiples of 10

f

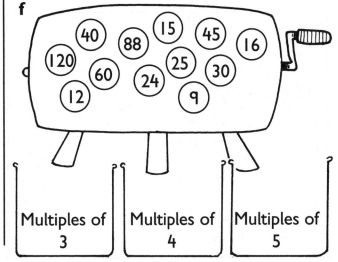

40 88 15 45 120 60 25 24 30 16 12 9

Multiples of 3   Multiples of 4   Multiples of 5

Collins Primary Maths © HarperCollinsPublishers Ltd 2000

Name _____ Date _____

Missing numbers

In each sequence below, each shape represents one number.
Work out the value of each shape by using the clues given.
Write the numbers inside the shapes.

1

$$\bigcirc + \boxed{} = \triangle$$

$$\tfrac{1}{2} \times 100 = \triangle$$

$$\boxed{} + \triangle = 74$$

$$\triangle - \boxed{} = \bigcirc$$

2

$$\diamondsuit \times \bigcirc = \boxed{} + \triangle$$

$$\diamondsuit + \triangle = 15$$

$$\bigcirc + \bigcirc = 8$$

$$\boxed{} - \diamondsuit = 13$$

3

$$\boxed{} + \boxed{} = \bigcirc - \triangle$$

$$\boxed{} \times 2 = 30$$

$$\bigcirc \div \boxed{} = 4$$

$$\triangle \times 2 = \bigcirc$$

4

$$\diamondsuit \div \bigcirc = \triangle \times \boxed{}$$

$$6 + \bigcirc = 9$$

$$\diamondsuit \div \triangle = 18$$

$$\bigcirc \times \boxed{} = 18$$

5

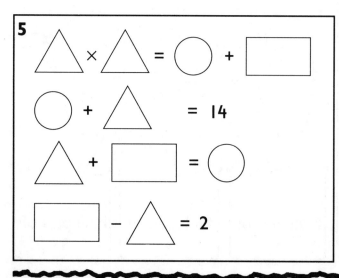

6

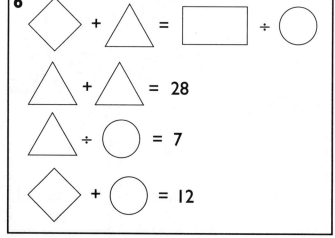

Collins Primary Maths © HarperCollins*Publishers* Ltd 2000

Name	Date

Simple sevens

A game for 2 – 3 players.

Instructions

● You need 36 counters.

● Cover each multiplication fact with a counter.

● Take turns to uncover a fact and give the answer.

● If the answer is correct, keep the counter.

● The player with the most counters at the end is the winner.

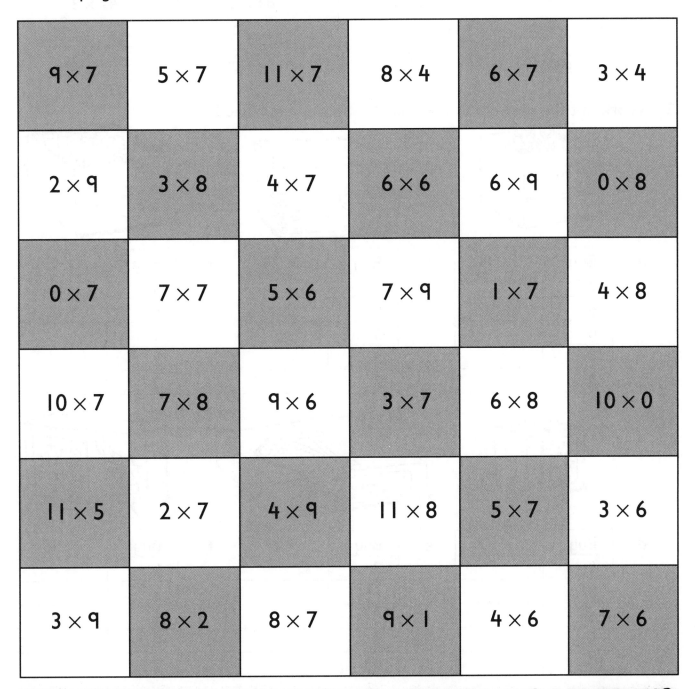

9 × 7	5 × 7	11 × 7	8 × 4	6 × 7	3 × 4
2 × 9	3 × 8	4 × 7	6 × 6	6 × 9	0 × 8
0 × 7	7 × 7	5 × 6	7 × 9	1 × 7	4 × 8
10 × 7	7 × 8	9 × 6	3 × 7	6 × 8	10 × 0
11 × 5	2 × 7	4 × 9	11 × 8	5 × 7	3 × 6
3 × 9	8 × 2	8 × 7	9 × 1	4 × 6	7 × 6

Collins Primary Maths © HarperCollinsPublishers Ltd 2000

Name _____ Date _____

Multiplying larger numbers

1 For each of the calculations below, approximate the answer and circle the number you think is closest to the actual answer.

a	b	c	d
64×4	73×5	46×9	37×6
60 600	350 400	540 450	300 180
240	280	400	240

e	f	g	h
58×8	49×7	83×3	42×3
500 400	400 300	200 240	80 120
600	350	270	150

2 Work out the answers to these calculations in your head.

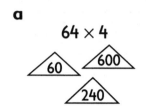 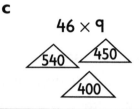 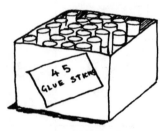

a	Buy	× 34
	3	
	6	
	4	
	5	
	9	

b	Buy	× 24
	6	
	4	
	3	
	5	
	7	

c	Buy	× 45
	3	
	6	
	5	
	4	
	2	

 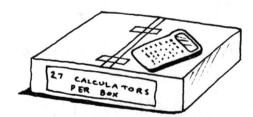 

d	Buy	× 53
	4	
	3	
	6	
	5	
	10	

e	Buy	× 27
	3	
	6	
	10	
	5	
	4	

f	Buy	× 36
	4	
	3	
	5	
	6	
	2	

Collins Primary Maths © HarperCollins*Publishers* Ltd 2000

Name _____ Date _____

Multiplication and division

Buy some lucky dip parcels from each stall.
Find the answer to each calculation.

a

Lucky Dip
× 10
× 100

$752 \times 100 = \boxed{}$

$27 \times 100 = \boxed{}$

$456 \times 10 = \boxed{}$

$168 \times 100 = \boxed{}$

$92 \times 10 = \boxed{}$

$460 \times 10 = \boxed{}$

b

Lucky Dip

÷ 10
÷ 100

$3000 \div 10 = \boxed{}$

$5000 \div 10 = \boxed{}$

$8000 \div 10 = \boxed{}$

$7000 \div 100 = \boxed{}$

$9000 \div 10 = \boxed{}$

$4000 \div 10 = \boxed{}$

c

Lucky Dip

Doubles

$95 \times 2 = \boxed{}$

$55 \times 2 = \boxed{}$

$80 \times 2 = \boxed{}$

$75 \times 2 = \boxed{}$

$35 \times 2 = \boxed{}$

$15 \times 2 = \boxed{}$

d

Lucky Dip

Halves

$150 \div 2 = \boxed{}$

$190 \div 2 = \boxed{}$

$180 \div 2 = \boxed{}$

$230 \div 2 = \boxed{}$

$270 \div 2 = \boxed{}$

$\frac{1}{2} \times 150 = \boxed{}$

d

Lucky Dip

× 3 × 4 × 5
× 6 × 7 × 8
× 9

$80 \times \boxed{} = 320$

$43 \times 6 = \boxed{}$

$68 \times \boxed{} = 272$

$19 \times \boxed{} = 95$

$72 \times 6 = \boxed{}$

$33 \times 8 = \boxed{}$

Collins Primary Maths © HarperCollinsPublishers Ltd 2000

Name _____ Date _____

Recording division

Choose your own starting numbers from those on the building bricks.

Choose your own divisor from the numbers on the cards.

Record 2 calculations for each set. Approximate the answer first and write it in the cloud.

a

3   4

84   48

72   96

4) 84

(20)

Answer =

)

Answer =

b

6   4

96   132

108   72

)

Answer =

)

Answer =

c

5   3

75   135

120   105

)

Answer =

)

Answer =

d

4   5

60   120

100   140

)

Answer =

)

Answer =

e

6   3

84

96   78

108

)

Answer =

)

Answer =

Name	Date

Heads up

1 Complete the sentences.

a

I in ____ coins are heads.

I head for every ____ tails.

b

____ in ____ coins are heads.

____ head for every ____ tails.

c

____ in ____ coins are heads.

____ heads for every ____ tail.

2 Write another sentence to describe the coins.

a I in 2 coins are heads.

I head for every ____ tails.

b I in 5 coins are heads.

_____

c I in 10 coins are heads.

_____

d 2 in 6 coins are heads.

_____

e 3 in 4 coins are heads.

_____

f 6 in 10 coins are heads.

_____

3 Write another sentence to describe the coins.

a I head for every 3 tails.

____ in ____ coins are heads.

b 2 heads for every 3 tails.

_____

c I head for every 7 tails.

_____

d 3 heads for every 3 tails.

_____

4 Draw coin patterns for questions 2 and 3.
Continue on the back of the sheet, if necessary.

Collins Primary Maths © HarperCollins*Publishers* Ltd 2000

Name _____ Date _____

Rugby decimals

1 Colour the rugby balls as described.

a

1 black for every 3 white.

b

3 black for every 7 white.

c

1 black for every 4 white.

d

3 black for every 1 white.

e

5 black for every 5 white.

f

2 black for every 3 white.

2 Describe each pattern in question 1 three more ways.

a _____	**b** _____
c _____	**d** _____
e _____	**f** _____

For example:

3 black for every 2 white.

3 out of 5 are black.

$\frac{3}{5}$ are black.

0·6 are black.

3 Describe these three different ways. If necessary use counters to help.

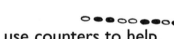

a $\frac{3}{4}$ are black.

    0·75 are black.

    3 out of 4 are black.

    3 black for every 1 white.

b $\frac{8}{10}$ are black.

c 1 out of 5 are black.

d 4 black for every 6 white.

e 0·25 are black.

f $\frac{2}{5}$ are black.

g 3 black for every 3 white.

h 1 out of 10 are black.

Collins Primary Maths © HarperCollinsPublishers Ltd 2000

Name _____ Date _____

Missing numbers

Work out the missing number using the written method of addition.

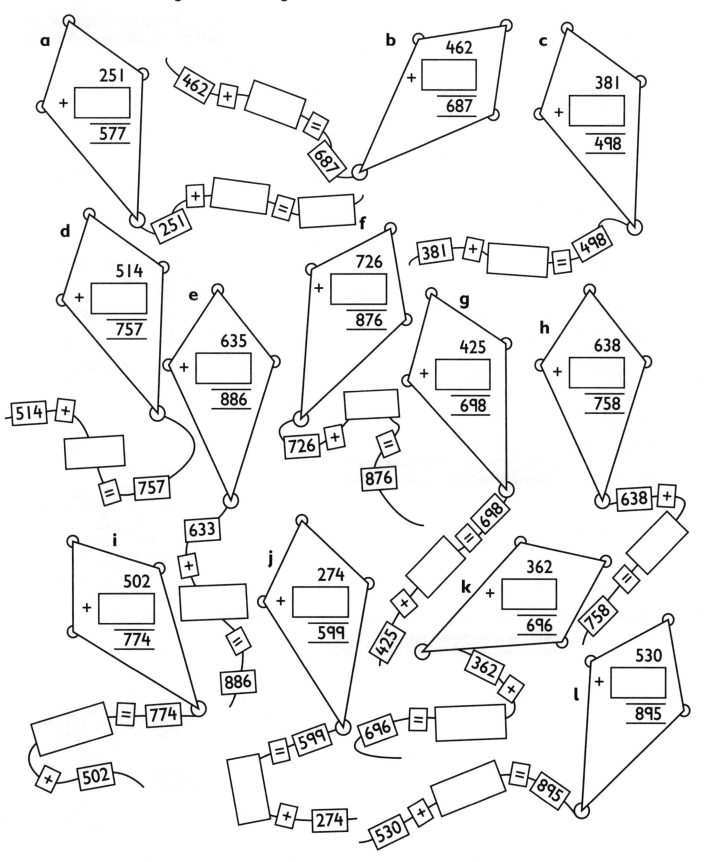

Name _____ Date _____

Travel Venn and Carroll diagrams

The children in Class 4B wrote down how they travel to school.

Simon	bus	$3\frac{1}{2}$ km	not alone
Vanessa	walk	2 km	alone
Rob	car	4 km	not alone
Narida	bus	3 km	not alone
Neil	walk	1 km	not alone
Harbans	walk	$\frac{1}{4}$ km	alone
Jill	bike	2 km	alone
Sanchez	car	6 km	not alone
Jasmine	walk	$1\frac{1}{4}$ km	alone
Kate	bus	5 km	not alone
Leroy	bus	$1\frac{1}{2}$ km	not alone
Yil Tong	car	$\frac{3}{4}$ km	not alone
Daniel	walk	$\frac{1}{2}$ km	alone
Andrew	walk	$1\frac{1}{4}$ km	alone
Michael	bus	$2\frac{1}{2}$ km	not alone
Charlie	bike	$\frac{1}{4}$ km	alone
David	bus	$1\frac{1}{4}$ km	not alone
Ella	walk	1 km	alone
Hank	bus	7 km	not alone

Questionnaire

(1) How do you travel to school?

(2) How far do you travel?

(3) Do you travel alone or not alone?

1 Make your own Carroll diagram to show how they travelled.

How class 4B travel to school	

2 Make your own Venn diagram to show how they travelled.

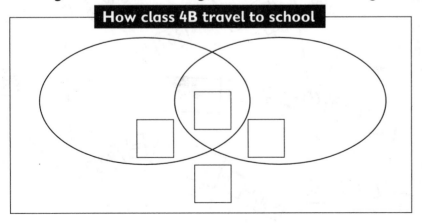

How class 4B travel to school

Collins Primary Maths © HarperCollins*Publishers* Ltd 2000